A Bike for Alex

Story by Elsie Nelley
Illustrations by Sharyn Madder

One day, Alex went next door
to see her friend Hannah.
Hannah was nine and Alex was six.

"Come and see my new bike,"
said Hannah.
"My old one is too small for me now,
and the brakes need fixing."

Hannah's mum came out
to see the girls.
She looked at Alex,
and she looked at the little bike.
"Hannah's little blue bike
would be just right for you,"
she said.
"Your dad is good at fixing things.
If he can fix the brakes,
you can have the bike."

Alex was so pleased.

Hannah helped Alex
to push the little bike
over to her place.

Alex showed it to Mum.

"You are lucky," said Mum.
"But let's put it in the shed.
I don't want you to ride it
if it's not safe.
Dad will have a good look at it
as soon as he can."

The next day,
when Alex got home from school,
she ran to look in the shed.

The bike was in bits
all over the floor.

"Oh, Dad!" she cried.
"Can't you fix it?"

"I hope I can," said Dad.
"But you will just have to wait
and see."

Alex didn't feel very happy.
She wanted a bike
that she could ride.

The next morning,
Alex went to see
if Dad had fixed the bike.
But he had gone to work,
and the door of the shed
was locked.

"I will have to wait all day for Dad
to get home," said Alex.

When Dad got home from work,
he opened the shed door.
Then he came out with the bike.

It was red now!

"Oh, thanks, Dad," said Alex.
"It looks just like a new bike."

"I fixed it for you last night,"
said Dad.
"Now you can ride it."

"Hannah, Hannah!" called Alex.
"Come and see my new bike."